Borderline Personality Disorder

A Guide to Understanding, Managing, and Treating BPD

Jessica Rose

Table of Contents

Introduction

Thank you for taking the time to read this book on Borderline Personality Disorder (BPD).

The following chapters will discuss what exactly borderline personality disorder is, the causes, the symptoms, and common treatments. It will also teach you alternative treatments for BPD and management techniques for both loved ones and sufferers. This book is an easy, user-friendly guide to breaking through the stigma of BPD and discovering the humanity and worth of the people who are impacted by BPD. Borderline personality disorder can be hard to manage, but with the right help, it is very treatable.

This book is meant to do much more than just tell you about BPD. It is intended to highlight the truths of BPD and dismiss the myths that are commonly associated with it. Throughout this book, efforts will be made to destigmatize this disorder and treat it with compassion.

There is no cure for BPD, but with treatment, people can lead ordinary lives that are free from the crippling doubts and fears that often accompany BPD. In the following chapters, we will discuss the various treatment options at length to help you gain an understanding of what might be most suitable for your own unique situation.

Remember, if at any point during this book you think that you may have borderline personality disorder – do not self-diagnose. Instead, discuss your concerns with a mental health professional who will be able to make an accurate diagnosis. Borderline personality disorder has a lot of similarities with other conditions, so be sure to receive an accurate diagnosis before beginning any specific treatments.

Thank you again for choosing this book. I hope you find it to be both helpful, and informative.

Chapter 1: The Basics of Borderline Personality Disorder

What Is Borderline Personality Disorder?

Borderline Personality Disorder (BPD) is a mental illness that many people experience. It was initially named BPD because professionals believed it to exist in the borderline between neurosis (mental conditions that don't include hallucinations) and psychosis (mental disorders that make people question reality), which psychologists have since debunked. It is also sometimes called emotionally unstable personality disorder or emotional dysregulation disorder. Historically, the research on BPD has been highly limited, but fortunately, researchers have been paying more attention to the disorder recently.

As the name would suggest, BPD is a personality disorder that is marked by long-term dysfunctional thoughts and behavior patterns. Generally, personality disorders are only experienced by adults or people in their late teens because these disorders take a while to establish themselves. Having a personality disorder doesn't mean your personality is awful or irredeemable; it only means that you experience interactions with yourself and the world around you differently to others. Frequently, people with personality disorders will have multiple conditions that culminate to create a personality disorder.

When people have BPD, they often feel like they are emotionally fragile. Little things can set them off into fits of rage or self-hate. They feel paranoid sometimes, and this paranoia can make it hard to have healthy relationships with other people, leading people with BPD to have intense but short relationships. Thus, BPD can make it hard for people to function normally without treatment. Luckily, treatment has been shown to help with the symptoms dramatically.

Generally, BPD first emerges when people are teenagers, with the intensity of the disorder changing over time. One of the most significant issues is that people often go undiagnosed or misdiagnosed, which can make it an almost insurmountable challenge to handle one's BPD. Understanding what the condition is and how it impacts people is useful knowledge that sufferers, loved ones, and the general public should all be aware of. The more people know about BPD, the easier treatment becomes.

While people can manage the condition and the symptoms can lessen, BPD is not curable at this time. Some people live their whole lives with untreated BPD, and this can make it hard to live a regular life, particularly when it comes to social or romantic relationships. It is never too late to treat BPD, but gaining a proper diagnosis and then beginning treatment as soon as possible will yield the best results.

Because of their mental dysfunction, people who have BPD can be impulsive, unpredictable, and in some cases, volatile. They can feel like they are an uncontrollable storm. Each time they try to reach out for the things that they want in life, they can feel rejection and self-loathing simply because they are not emotionally prepared for the tumult that life brings. While people with BPD regularly get a reputation for being narcissistic, in reality they are often highly empathetic. Paradoxically, they can become self-involved and struggle to see things through the perspectives of others. The challenging, emotional aspects of this disorder can sometimes inhibit empathy. Nevertheless, people with BPD feel things deeply, to the point that understanding and regulating their emotions becomes overwhelming. This can make it hard for them to deal with the feelings of others despite wanting to help.

Further, people with BPD are prone to obsession. They easily become attached to people, things, or ideas. These obsessions can often fuel their impulsivity, which sends them spiraling further into their obsession. For example, someone with BPD may be a compulsive shopper, and when they start to shop, they may have trouble stopping.

People with BPD may have reoccurring feelings of emptiness, and understandably they wish to fill that void. This feeling of emptiness, again, encourages their harmful behaviors. They'll desperately try to feel better, but then, they will engage in situations that only make their situation worse.

The exact causes of BPD are unknown, but people with BPD have often experienced past abuse or trauma. These incidents can make them feel worthless, unlovable, and abandoned; all feelings that are common among those with BPD. It is most likely caused by a combination of childhood factors, social factors, and genetic factors.

BPD is also commonly comorbid with several conditions, meaning that it exists alongside them. People with BPD often experience substance abuse issues, anxiety, depression, self-harm, and eating disorders. They also may experience conditions like bipolar disorder or post-traumatic stress disorder (PTSD). Oftentimes, those same conditions that can be comorbid with BPD will have overlapping symptoms with BPD, making it particularly challenging to receive an accurate diagnosis.

BPD is a disorder that has a huge stigma, with people often associating this disorder with rage, selfishness, and danger. While BPD does present several real challenges for patients, it is largely misunderstood. BPD isn't a particular type of person; instead, it is a condition that has shared mental behaviors. How people with BPD act can vary significantly based on their personalities and how they have learned to deal with their symptoms.

Who It Impacts

Researchers have estimated that BPD impacts anywhere from one-point-six percent of the population to just over five percent. Unfortunately, BPD is one of the most stigmatized mental health disorders; thus, the understanding of it by the public, and even by mental health professionals, is frequently lacking.

Women are mostly diagnosed with BPD, with men only being diagnosed twenty-five percent of the time; however, experts believe that there is less of a gender gap among people who have the disorder, but practitioners commonly misdiagnose men. Doctors regularly will tell men that they have depression or PTSD rather than borderline personality disorder.

Anyone can develop BPD once they have reached adulthood. It is not limited by race, gender, or any other distinguishing factor. Those aspects can have a role in the development of BPD due to social factors, but they are not themselves going to cause BPD. Moreover, BPD does not indicate whether people are moral or not. Having BPD will not inherently make a person good or evil, so it is essential to recognize that most people with BPD are predominately good people who are simply trying to handle an overwhelm of confusing emotions. BPD is not easy to live with, especially for people who have yet to be treated, so it is best to treat BPD sufferers with patience and care.

Chapter 2: Signs and Symptoms of BPD

Diagnostic Criteria

There are nine factors that professionals consider when diagnosing BPD, and these factors are the core components of the disorder. These signs and symptoms are the primary behaviors you will see in people that are diagnosed with Borderline Personality Disorder. To be diagnosed with BPD, people have to exhibit five of the following tendencies. If you recognize that you have 5 or more of these symptoms, you may possibly have BPD, but you will need to see a mental health professional to receive a proper diagnosis.

Fear of Abandonment

People with BPD may fear that they will be abandoned by anyone they become close to. They may feel like it is only a matter of time before someone realizes that there is something wrong with them and leaves. This fear often stems from childhood abandonment issues, but this isn't always the case. People with BPD often feel that they are unworthy of other people sticking around. They become convinced that they are living on borrowed time and that people will abandon them sooner rather than later.

Regardless of whether they are genuinely at risk of being abandoned or not, the mere sense of abandonment can be debilitating for a person with BPD. For example, a person with BPD may take someone saying that they can't come to a planned social event because they are sick as abandonment, even though that wasn't the other person's intention. The individual with BPD can easily become paranoid and begin to think that other people are making excuses because they don't want to see them.

This fear of abandonment can make it hard for people with BPD to maintain healthy relationships. They can easily become convinced that their significant others are cheating or are planning on breaking up with them, even if there is no proof to support these fears. This can cause them to make desperate efforts to keep the other person in their lives, even if those efforts are harmful to their well-being. The desperate attempts of a person with BPD often lead to self-sabotage. Through their desperation, they make the other person feel insecure in the relationship or even attacked by the BPD person, which does not bode well for the relationship heading into the future.

Unstable Relationships

Another common trait of people with BPD is having unstable relationships. This includes romantic, platonic, and sexual relationships. People with BPD are susceptible to feeling unsure about their relationships, and will either try to prevent the relationship from ending, or they will finish it when it becomes too overwhelming for them. They will see their relationships as being either wonderful or awful, with very little in-between. They'll see black and white without any gradient. They will feel either accepted or rejected, loved or hated, engaged or detached. For people with BPD, it is hard to see the in-betweens that are more common than polarity.

Changing Self-Image or Identity

People with BPD may not have a good sense of who they are. Their view of themselves may rapidly change. They may look in the mirror and feel self-assured in the morning but then hate themselves by night. They often have a fragile relationship with their identities, and while they want to know who they are, they cannot seem to figure it out. If they are not themselves, no one can entirely reject them. After all, you cannot reject someone you don't know.

Their interests can change in a flash. They can go from loving knitting to suddenly wanting to get into baking instead. They may hop from hobby to hobby without settling on one long enough to build skill and connection to that hobby. They may question even the most fundamental parts of themselves. For example, a person with BPD may doubt their sexuality and wonder if maybe they are wrong about the types of people that they are sexually drawn to.

The lack of a stable identity can cause some problems to be worsened. People with BPD may turn to the wrong sources to find their identity. They may use other people to define themselves and lose sight of the things that interest them and make them feel passionate. Thus, they will feel even more hollowness. They will feel like they are without personalities or any genuine interests, which can lead to depression and other mental health issues.

Impulsive Behaviors

People with BPD are prone to being impulsive. They will do things without giving it much thought. In doing this, they can temporarily fill a void that they feel. There are various impulsive behaviors that are common among people with BPD. Some of the most problematic behaviors include substance abuse and risky driving. Other impulsive behaviors that medical professionals will look for include compulsive shopping, binge eating, and risky sexual behavior. Anything that you can do in excess or that is inherently dangerous can count as impulsive. While people with BPD often don't like their impulses, they feel powerless to them.

Self-Harm

Self-harm is one of the more directly harmful components of BPD. While not all people with BPD self-harm, many do. Self-harm includes anything that you can do to hurt yourself. Common methods of self-harm include cutting, burning, hitting, and head-banging. There are nearly endless methods that people can use to harm themselves. Some of the impulsive behaviors would also count as self-harming behaviors. Harmful sex, for example, can be used as a self-harm tactic, even though some unaware people don't recognize it as such. Even small things like picking a scab to hurt yourself can be considered as self-injurious.

Suicidal Thoughts or Behaviors

People with BPD commonly will have suicidal thoughts, or worse, they will have suicidal actions. It is not uncommon for people with BPD to attempt suicide, and unfortunately, some people are successful. People with BPD may also threaten suicide as a way of keeping people in their lives or avoiding rejection. While this behavior seems malicious, it is usually out of desperation more than wanting to be harmful. Even if they are just threats designed to keep someone from leaving, these behaviors and thoughts should always be taken seriously. Do not shrug them off as just attention-seeking behavior.

Moodiness

Rapidly changing moods are a common occurrence with BPD. People will feel happy in one moment and then feel attacked and rejected by something as innocuous as a facial expression the next. People with BPD will become irritable quickly, and after outbursts, they may overcompensate and try to act nicer or happier to try to restore a balance and avoid the negative fallout of their moodiness. It can be challenging for people with BPD to navigate and express what they are feeling.

Anger

People with BPD often feel extensive anger. This anger does not mean that they are violent or even that they will yell. This anger is often rooted in their insecurities, and it can be expressed in several ways. Some people with BPD will have explosive anger, but other people will take that anger out on themselves.

Dissociation

People with BPD also commonly dissociate. Dissociation is similar to an out of body experience. When you dissociate, you feel disconnected to yourself or your surroundings. Everything around you may feel surreal, or you may even feel drained of all life. Many people describe it as though they are watching themselves, but that is not how everyone experiences it. Fundamentally, it is the feeling that you and reality aren't quite connected. Extreme dissociation is often a result of trauma, especially sexual trauma or an abusive upbringing, but dissociation happens to everyone. If you've ever driven home and it was so automatic that you didn't remember the process, that is a similar feeling to dissociation.

Other Signs

There are some other signs beyond these nine hallmarks. These signs are not part of the diagnostic criteria, but they often are related to those nine markers. They give a better idea of how borderline people behave. Further, they can help you analyze whether you or a loved one has BPD. Again, simply having a few symptoms doesn't mean that you necessarily have BPD. There is no official medical test for BPD, so a diagnosis is up to the judgment of a professional. Some professionals who don't specialize in BPD may not realize what you have and misdiagnose you. Thus, if you have several of these signs, ensure that you are speaking with a professional who understands BPD.

Impulsivity may make it hard for people with BPD to control their behaviors. Impulsivity can occur in a variety of ways. Still, in general, it is the idea that people with BPD will be more prone to acting on their urges without fully contemplating the results. Note that people with BPD won't necessarily be impulsive in all areas of their lives. For example, someone with

BPD may be cautious with their money, while that same person may be impulsive with their driving or substance use. Similarly, a person who makes hasty relationship decisions might be careful with parenting decisions. Impulsivity does not always mean that a person with BPD is dangerous, because they can express their impulsivity in various ways.

People with BPD often idealize and devalue people. Idealization is the idea of making someone more perfect than they are in your mental process, while devaluation is taking away their good qualities and filling your perception of them with only negativity. These two terms are opposites, and people with BPD often suffer from black and white thinking, so they see things as either perfect or worthless. They can inadvertently do this with people too. For example, they may see their best friend as the most remarkable human on earth one minute and then the worst in the next moment. When they feel rejected or abandoned, they may attribute their negative feelings to another person's wrongness rather than facing their own feelings of inferiority.

They will persistently struggle to maintain their relationships. This struggle to maintain relationships is one of the most prominent facets of BPD. People with BPD will often self-sabotage relationships, or they will cling onto relationships that don't benefit them. They have a deep desire to belong and to be loved unconditionally, and they will go to unhealthy lengths to satisfy those feelings. Unfortunately, with untreated BPD, they often never find the relationships that they are looking for.

BPD sufferers may also struggle to maintain good boundaries with the people in their lives. They can be susceptible to unhealthy or abusive relationships because they are so desperate to be loved and to have people stay that they will open themselves up to being abused. Some would rather be hurt than abandoned, so they will let partners or other people in their lives overstep their boundaries.

Because they have a hard time with boundaries, some people with BPD may become codependent. Codependency is when partners, or two people in a close relationship, rely heavily on each other for psychological support. It often happens when people are in relationships with an addict, but it can happen to any two people who rely too heavily on one another to feel complete. Because of their need to be wanted and loved, people with BPD can easily fall into these relationships. They let themselves become completely attached to a person to the point that they can't detach themselves from the other person. They rely on the other person to define who they are and even how they feel. It's so easy for them to get lost in the other person, and this puts them in danger of losing what little sense of self they have. This codependency can quickly become toxic and will be very hard for the BPD person to leave.

People with BPD often have low self-esteem. Because of all their fears, they start to question their own worth. They think that no one will ever truly love them for who they are. They sometimes feel that they have to hide themselves to be liked, and because they feel empty, they can feel that they have no personality. They doubt themselves and their value to others. Even when they do exceptional work, they may feel like failures simply because they assume that everything they do is wrong or will be rejected by their peers. This way of living is terrifying, and it can be challenging for people with BPD to believe in themselves or realize their potential.

Some BPD patients may struggle to focus. They become so wrapped up in their personal world or become so paranoid that they can have trouble concentrating on anything else. They become obsessed with things that they think can bring them happiness to the point that they struggle to tear their minds from those things. This obsession can lead to them being detail-oriented in some areas while completely neglecting others. You can find this symptom in other disorders such as depression or ADHD, but it is also common in BPD.

BPD people can also feel emotions more intensely than other people. They feel threatened quickly, and they can go from feeling content to feeling incredibly distressed in an instant.

People often experience BPD in a cyclical nature. They feel bad, so they turn to actions that can temporarily make them feel better. In the end, the semblance of feeling excellent and self-assured is always broken because they haven't dealt with their deeper issues. Thus, they begin the cycle again and consistently end up feeling rejected or worthless. They jump from highs to lows and back again, rarely experiencing a moment of emotional stability.

Types of BPD

Some types of BPD are not specific diagnoses, but they can help describe different people whose BPD may show itself in various ways. Some people may not realize they have BPD because their symptoms don't present in the way that people traditionally stereotype BPD. These classifications may show you how you can still have BPD without having all the classic symptoms or having them show as they commonly do. The renowned psychologist, Theodore Millon, established these different types of BPD. Some professionals may add or use other types, but these are the most prevalent.

Discouraged

The discouraged form of BPD often includes dependent people. These people tend to become highly dependent on others for their own self-worth and decision-making. They can become dependent on people who they don't even know that well. These people are known for becoming clingy and wanting to hold onto the relationships that they have, desperately. They are less likely to give up on a relationship and will instead try to cling onto it and change themselves to fit what they think the other person needs. These patients often use self-harm to deal with their pain and other feelings. They most prominently feel as though they will never be good enough. While they don't show anger as much as other types, they will have extensive hidden aggression.

This type is most prone to becoming codependent, and in their relationships, they will struggle to separate themselves from the other person. They can have some overlap with people who have Dependent Personality Disorder. They conform to their environments and do not embrace their individuality in fear that they will be rejected.

This type is also sometimes called the "quiet" type because the symptoms may not be as apparent. This is due to the sufferer bending to societal and interpersonal expectations. These people rarely let their anger out, and instead tend to keep it hidden from the rest of the world, which makes it hard for them to cope with their feelings. Like the self-destructive type, they often take their anger out on themselves. This type is prone to feeling both shame and guilt because they blame themselves whenever bad things happen. They are also more prone to dissociation. These people may seem the highest functioning of all the types.

Petulant

Petulant borderline individuals are the type of person who is hard to please. Their wants will change often and based on their moods, so nothing is ever right for this type. They will get angry and express their anger externally. When a petulant borderline doesn't get their way, they become irrationally upset. Sometimes, their anger will be more covert with their loved ones. They often are passive-aggressive and struggle to show the full breadth of their anger. At times, their rage will be loud and uncontrollable. This type is often marked by being unmovable, defensive, and pigheaded. These people hate to say that they made a mistake or outwardly admit that they were wrong. However, when they are wrong, they feel as though they are worthless despite mistakes being a normal part of life.

This type can be pessimistic, and they will struggle to maintain relationships because they will want to depend on other people. They will also often push themselves away because they fear that they will not be worthy of a friendship or intimate relationship. They will hold grudges against people who they fear have wronged them, and they will struggle to see the full perspective of a situation. Thus, they can be judgmental without meaning to be. These people want to feel worthy, but they often feel as though people will disappoint them and not fulfill their needs.

Impulsive

Impulsive borderline is a type of BPD that can seem the most extraverted. These people are often the life of the party, and they can seem incredibly charming to the people around them. At the same time, they are volatile. They can go from having a good time to being incredibly angry. They are prone to boredom and will use impulsive behavior to fill the boredom that they feel. They will turn to drugs, sex, and reckless behaviors to feel alive and break through the chronic numbness they feel. They sometimes will also have antisocial personality disorder or antisocial tendencies.

People with this type of BPD love to be in the limelight. If the attention is not on them, they may start to feel upset and lash out, engaging in even more reckless behaviors. These people struggle to contemplate the results of their actions, and they are especially prone to addictive behaviors. Impulsive borderline people can make decisions that jeopardize their relationships with other people, but they may also end up harming themselves without meaning to. These people need to feel eyes on them. They don't like to be ignored, and when they are (or think they are), they will lash out. These thrill-seekers will go to harmful lengths to feel temporary fulfillment.

This type of BPD people is often captivating. They can draw people in and make those people feel wonderful. They can make jokes and act bright and cheery, but their good humor can break when someone tries to take away the attention or rejects the BPD person.

Self-Destructive

The final type of BPD is the self-destructive type. As you can guess, this type often tries to destroy themselves. They are prone to self-harm, and they tend to act in ways that threaten their well-being. Sometimes, these actions are intentional, but other times they are subconscious. This type feels just as much anger as the other types, but they are more likely to take their rage out on themselves. People with this type of BPD can struggle to get help because so many of their problems and feelings are deeply embedded in their unconscious. They struggle to understand themselves because their sense of identity is so skewed and inconsistent. They don't know who they are, which makes it hard for them to understand their feelings.

These people are often resentful, moody, and no matter how much they try, they can't keep their anger away. They have deep levels of self-hate that makes them prone to do things like engage in harmful sex, self-mutilate, or demean themselves. They don't like the feeling of these actions, but they feel they are deserved and sometimes want to punish themselves for being so awful. They may show outbursts of rage, but the majority of their actions will be internalized.

Issues That Go Hand in Hand With BPD

People who have BPD are prone to having other comorbid disorders. Thus, they may have multiple severe mental health disorders that interact with one another and make functioning as well as recovery harder. It helps to be aware of the disorders that most commonly exist alongside BPD. You do not have to have any of these issues to have BPD, but if you do, treating your BPD can also help to treat the following problems. Nevertheless, you will want to address the other issues as well to ensure an optimal recovery.

The reason that so many people with BPD have other disorders is that BPD people have trouble regulating their moods, which can result in developing mood disorders or anxiety disorders. Further, the impulsivity of BPD can result in making negative choices with substances, including drugs, alcohol, and even food. People with BPD are desperately looking for ways to feel better about themselves and their social situations, which can result in them turning to unhealthy coping mechanisms or thought process. These issues only make it harder for them to use reason and treat themselves the way that they deserve to be treated.

If you or a loved one has any of the following issues, they can sometimes resemble BPD without being BPD, so while they can be comorbid, they can also exist alone and have some overlap with BPD symptoms. Thus, it is paramount to get a diagnosis from a mental health professional before proceeding with treatment because different treatment styles will be required based on the specific conditions you have. Comorbid disorders can make treatment more challenging because of the way disorders influence one another, but by knowing which ones you or a loved one has, you are taking a huge step forward towards better treatment outcomes.

Self-Worth Issues

One of the most significant issues that people with BPD face is self-worth issues. This issue is not a specific psychological diagnosis, but it does indicate that someone has issues that they need to resolve. Self-worth is our ability to find the inherent value within ourselves, even when we make mistakes or otherwise are flawed. Self-worth often correlates to self-esteem, which is the overall feeling we have about ourselves and our abilities. Unfortunately, people with BPD often have a hard time valuing themselves, which can lead to several problems like depression or anxiety.

People who have high self-esteem can feel good about their interactions with other people. They can go out in the world feeling confident and self-assured. Confidence makes it easier to take chances and venture outside your comfort zone. Self-esteem is vital to any person's well-being and is the formation of their sense of self. If you have little self-esteem, it's hard to know who you are, let alone what you want or what is right for you. Confidence is associated with accomplishment, so if you don't have it, it may be harder for you to reach goals. Further, people who aren't self-assured may not even set goals in the first place.

People with BPD may have moments of self-confidence where they can perform grandiose actions, especially if they also have Narcissistic Personality Disorder. Nevertheless, despite momentary rushes where they might feel good about themselves because of praise or a job well done on a project, their mood can quickly turn into one of self-hate when they realize that they've made a mistake. While it's normal to have imperfections and fail sometimes, BPD sufferers often take those things as failures of them as people. They think that their mistakes mean they are universally bad people. Thus, any small thing can send a person with BPD's identity into question, making them feel incompetent and insecure.

Substance Abuse

When you have BPD, you need to be incredibly careful with the substances you use, because substance abuse is one of the most common co-occurring conditions with BPD. Substance abuse is when people use substances (like drugs, including legal ones like alcohol) in ways that are harmful to themselves. People who abuse substances can become addicted, both physically and mentally, and this addiction can quickly ruin their lives. Because of their impulsivity, people with BPD are prone to using substances to escape their feelings. When people have BPD, they are emotionally compromised in ways that make substance abuse more appealing. They want an escape from themselves, and substances can numb them from their negative feelings.

Not only are people with BPD more prone to substance abuse, but substances can also worsen some of the most negative BPD symptoms. For example, when a person with BPD drinks way too much alcohol, they may become more volatile. They might become enraged and act on their rage, or they may get incredibly depressed. Substances can change the mind so that it is more prone to acting on impulse, and higher impulsiveness is never good for someone with BPD. When BPD sufferers abuse substances, they may engage in further self-harm and have a more challenging time knowing when to stop. They may also try to kill themselves when they are in an altered state.

Substances promise people with BPD a feeling other than emptiness. BPD sufferers often try to find ways to fill the hollowness they feel, but substances do more harm than good, and they also fail to address the core of the problem.

Eating Disorders

Eating disorders are one of the common co-occurring conditions that can exist among BPD patients. Some studies estimate that nearly fifty-four percent of people with BPD can also be diagnosed with comorbid eating disorders. Eating disorders are conditions that cause people to try to control their food intake to change their bodies and transform their self-image. These disorders are about much more than the body shape, though. They are often focused on one's sense of self-worth. Unexpectedly, people can feel more valued and powerful when they try to take charge of food. Attempts to control food can lead to harmful coping mechanisms that are experienced through various eating disorders. Eating disorders are more than just diets. People with eating disorders spend hours thinking about food, and they put their bodies at great risk.

BPD sufferers can have any of the eating disorders. Experts estimate that just over twenty percent of sufferers have anorexia nervosa, a condition characterized by low body weight and food restriction. Meanwhile, patients with BPD and bulimia nervosa had a prevalence of twenty-four percent. Bulimia is characterized by binging and purging. Less clear statistics are available for other eating disorders, including binge eating disorder (BED), which is more common than anorexia or bulimia. BED is a disorder that includes binging without compensatory methods. Finally, some patients may experience Otherwise Specified Feeding or Eating Disorders (OSFED), which can consist of patients who do not fit into the diagnostic criteria of the other conditions perfectly. Any eating disorder is harmful, and BPD only serves to fuel them.

When people have BPD, they often feel awful about themselves. Accordingly, they may try anything to feel a sense of belonging and worth. Eating disorders can give them a semblance of control for periods of time, but they can also make them feel like they are doing what they have to do to be loved and accepted by the people around them.

Depression

Depression and other mood disorders are common among BPD patients. Depression is having an extended time of lowered mood that can occur for various reasons such as trauma, grief, or brain chemistry. Some research estimates that depression or other mood disorders can be found in ninety-six percent of people with BPD. Eighty-three percent of BPD patients meet the qualifications for major depression, and an additional thirty-nine percent could be classified as having dysthymic disorder (which is chronic depression that tends to be less severe). Evidently, depression is often seen with BPD, which makes sense, given that seven percent of the population experiences depression. With so much prevalence in the general population, it doesn't come as a shock that depression and BPD often overlap.

While it is normal for these conditions to be comorbid, some people with BPD won't experience depression. Those with depression may still have depressive symptoms because of the unstable moods caused by BPD, but they will not be otherwise depressed. Having low moods, even if they are frequent, does not necessarily mean that you are depressed. These moods can be caused by BPD alone or by similar conditions like bipolar disorder. Nevertheless, depression is likely in BPD patients, so it is something to keep in mind.

Depression can have a variety of symptoms. It doesn't always have to be feeling sad. Some people with depression will feel restless, bored, or angry rather than sad or tired. When you have depression, you don't feel like yourself. You feel like you can't entirely access happiness, which is a worry that people with BPD often have. BPD sufferers can become hopeless as all their relationships crumble, and they struggle to act normally. The more people experience BPD without treatment, the harder it can be for them to keep their heads up and feel like things can get better. This mindset makes them more prone to a declined mood. Further, unprocessed trauma can have similarly depressing results. Thus, many facets of BPD create a perfect storm to cause depression.

Anxiety

Anxiety is one of the most common conditions that people have, so you can expect that people in the BPD community would also have it in high quantities. Because they feel so much mental uncertainty, people with BPD will be very fear-driven, which is associated with anxiety. The fears that people have that are caused by BPD can quickly blossom into other worries that are debilitating and make it hard to function in the world. These fears can make it hard for people with BPD to seek treatment and make the necessary changes that they need to transform their lives.

People with BPD are anxious about many parts of their lives. They tend to be particularly worried about relationships and other social interactions. They fear that other people will never love them, which causes a myriad of anxious responses. They are often socially anxious and worry about how their behavior with other people will impact the way other people view them. They become obsessed with how they are perceived because they struggle to determine what their identities are. Thus, the opinions of the people around them become essential in the way they feel about themselves.

If you have anxiety and BPD, treating the BPD will help the anxiety because you'll learn to accept the fears that you have, and to reduce some of the interpersonal concerns that are so prevalent in people with BPD. You may have some lingering anxiety even after the BPD is treated, but if you are aware of your anxiety, you can better manage it. Everyone has anxiety from time to time, but only certain people will have anxiety that rises to the level of an anxiety disorder. Thus, you will have to have further conversations with a professional to identify if you have anxiety beyond just the normal scope of BPD.

PTSD

Traumatic experiences can trigger Post-Traumatic Stress Disorder (PTSD), so it can co-occur with BPD. Still, these conditions can look like one another without being co-occurring, so it's essential to identify which condition or conditions you are experiencing. Research has put the rate of co-occurrence of these disorders between twenty-five to sixty percent, which is a considerable number because, in the general population, the prevalence of these conditions separately is less than ten percent. Thus, the conditions clearly have important links that researchers need to continue to study.

Among people with PTSD and people with BPD, trauma can cause people's brains to react in unexpected and sometimes harmful ways to deal with trauma. Both conditions can include dissociation, moodiness, and feelings of being abandoned. People who have both conditions tend to have exacerbated symptoms, like the inability to regulate moods (affect dysregulation), dissociation, intrusive thoughts, self-harm, and suicidal behaviors. Further, those people who have both tend to have experienced their trauma when they were younger, though this is not always the case.

Another issue with these disorders co-occurring is that people with BPD may, through their impulsivity, end up in situations that put them at risk and more prone to PTSD. For example, someone with BPD may decide to get into a car with a drunk driver. They may end up in a traumatic crash that leaves them with PTSD. In another example, someone with BPD may be sexually impulsive and end up in a non-consensual situation. By no means should the person with BPD be victim-blamed for the things that other people do to them, but their impulsivity can put them in dangerous situations.

Chapter 3: Common Treatments for BPD

BPD cannot simply be cured by using a medication, though this can be very helpful with some symptoms. Generally, the ideal treatment method will include therapy or other skills management efforts. There are several types of therapy that BPD patients typically receive, and these types include both psychodynamic therapy and cognitive behavioral therapy subdivisions. Treatment types work differently based on the individual, so if you suffer from BPD, it may take some exploration to see what helps you best with your most prominent issues.

Some patients with BPD may need to be placed in a hospital, depending on the severity of their symptoms and comorbidity. Nevertheless, for many people, treatment can be outpatient, and it can be relatively unobtrusive in patients' lives. Consulting with a mental health professional can help you understand the level of care that you need, and what kind of care is most suitable. You may not find a treatment professional who you click with right away, but in time, you will find the proper treatment balance for yourself or your loved one.

Dialectical Behavior Therapy

Dialectical behavior therapy (DBT) is a therapy style that was created by Marcha Linehan, a mental health expert who made it specifically for the treatment of BPD, but mental health professionals also use it for other conditions. As a type of cognitive-behavioral therapy, DBT is a talk therapy that uses cognition as the main root of the treatment. Cognition is the perception you have of your own mental thought processes. You can figure out your cognition through your actions, perspectives, ideas, and senses. DBT tweaks the ideas of CBT to customize them for people with borderline personality disorder.

Patients have seen extraordinary results with DBT because it was created with the emotional issues of BPD in mind. This therapy focuses on issues that likely are rooted in biological, childhood, and personality factors. Thus, DBT was designed to help patients reduce their emotional dysregulation through skills that can help them healthily deal with their intense feelings. This method uses a variety of techniques such as individual therapy, group therapy, and help over the phone. Patients in DBT are required track their behaviors and become more aware of their actions and feelings. When they monitor how they are doing, they become more self-aware and will gain more from the therapy.

There are several skills that DBT teaches people to help them learn to deal with their emotions. The first skill is mindfulness and meditation. These skills are essential for people with BPD because mindfulness and meditation allows people to recognize their feelings without judging them. Another major skill deals with teaching patients how to regulate their emotions. They learn to be more aware of their feelings, and how to deal with those feelings before they get out of control. Another skill that people with DBT curate is interpersonal skills that allow them to communicate and handle friction in relationships. Finally, a fourth skill that people learn in DBT is distress tolerance. Distress tolerance is the idea that people can handle emotional distress while abstaining from negative behaviors that will worsen their condition long-term, such as self-harm or impulsive behaviors.

The research has shown how effective DBT is. Clinical trials have shown amazing results among patients. Being older than many newer treatments, it is well-established and has had more research done on it than some of the alternative methods for treating BPD. DBT is incredibly impactful for some of the more harmful symptoms of BPD. Studies have shown a stark difference in suicidal and self-harming behaviors among those who were treated with DBT. Further, DBT has consistently been able to reduce the substance abuse issue among BPD patients. It also teaches them how to deal with difficult emotions. People who have received DBT treatment also have fewer hospitalizations related to their BPD. Research shows that while BPD cannot be cured, seventy-seven percent of people who seek DBT treatment can reduce their symptoms within one year. In some cases, they can reduce their symptoms to the point that the patients no longer meet the BPD criteria! Even among the remaining patients, significant progress can be made in a year and with continued treatment.

If you are interested in a treatment that professionals have created specifically for people with BPD, DBT is one of the best options that you can choose. While this method does take a lot of work, it can result in a stark decrease in symptoms within a single year. Among all the treatments for BPD, DBT is the most widespread and has been acknowledged as the gold standard.

Mentalization-Based Treatment

Another standard treatment method for BPD is Mentalization-Based Treatment (MBT). MBT uses an evidence-based, sensible approach that isn't as varied as DBT. While DBT will require lots of paperwork and communication with mental health professionals, MBT is much simpler. MBT is a method that focuses on your wants and your feelings, and it determines how these mentalities correlate to how you behave. It focuses on the idea that your actions are separate from your thoughts and emotions. You may not always vocalize how you feel, but you can get some insight into those feelings through how you and the people around you behave. While behavior and emotions are separate and don't always line up, they are connected.

Peter Fonagy and Anthony Bateman established this method of treatment for BPD, and they claim that BPD is rooted in people being unable to mentalize as a result of their relationships in childhood. They think that people struggle to mentalize when they have an issue with their relationship with a caregiver. This idea stems from the concept that childhood issues fuel BPD. This theory is not something that everyone believes in, but for people who have abandonment issues with, this method has proven to be very helpful. While this process believes that childhood issues are the cause of BPD, it focuses on the present. In this treatment, your therapist usually won't give their opinions or input, but instead, will guide you through exercises.

Schema-Focused Therapy

Schema-focused therapy is a kind of psychotherapy that is often used for BPD. It blends methods of cognitive-behavioral therapy with other treatment methods to customize treatment for patients' unique psychological needs. As the name would imply, this therapy focuses on schemas, which are cognitive patterns that overarch your life. Some people have maladaptive schemas that people can trigger when they encounter certain events that remind them of the past. These maladaptive schemas lead to harmful behaviors that arise from our unhelpful thinking patterns. Thus, people with harmful schemas can respond in ways that are different from how people would normally behave. This type of therapy believes that people with BPD were influenced by childhood experiences such as abuse or other trauma that led to them creating problematic schemas.

Schema-focused treatment focuses on figuring out how the past impacts the present. It looks at people's schemas and tries to break them down for the patient. In the process of understanding schemas, people learn to adjust the methods they use to cope. They learn to release their negative feelings and alter the way that they are programmed to think.

Unfortunately, there hasn't been a whole lot of research to show how effective this method of treatment is for people with BPD. One study has shown that patients who used this treatment were able to lessen their symptoms greatly, but the evidence is not conclusive, and it will take more time to see how effective this treatment is for BPD.

Transference-Focused Therapy

Transference-focused therapy is a psychodynamic therapy that has been marked as a potentially excellent method for treating BPD and other personality disorders. It uses psychoanalytical thinking processes to help patients. Therapists are more active in this process, and they do not just sit and listen to patients. Instead, they play a more engaged role than in some other types of therapy. This therapy focuses on internal experiences as the reason for external behaviors. It also focuses on the patient and the therapist working together, encouraging the patient to transfer thoughts from their mind to the therapist, who can help them deal with ideas that the patient might not fully understand.

Transference is the idea that people will project how they are feeling or thinking onto others, and this happens when they talk to their therapist as well. This type of therapy doesn't try to fight the transference, and instead it aims to use the transference to understand the destructive behaviors of the client. Therapists focus on how patients can create positive changes in their lives, rather than addressing pathological issues directly.

This type of therapy involves having sessions twice a week to help patients work through their symptoms and make sense of how they are feeling. Patients are taught to connect with their identities and learn constructive rather than destructive habits. Transference-focused therapy has shown results in several studies, mainly when applied to destructive behaviors. It can be great for people who need intensive treatment but without the major commitment of CBT. This therapy is one of the lesser-known treatment options, but it does have a lot of potential.

Chapter 4: Alternative and Supplemental Treatments for BPD

These treatments have not been shown to be as effective as traditional treatments associated with BPD, but they have proven to have some degree of effectiveness. Researchers continue to explore how new treatment options can provide patients and loved one's with better outcomes. While these alternatives may not be right for everyone, you may find that they are suitable for your particular situation. Some of these treatments can also be used in conjunction with more traditional therapies, so they can add to your conventional treatment experience to provide better results overall. As with any treatment, it is up to you, and your medical team, to decide what is best for your situation.

STEPPS

STEPPS is an acronym that stands for Systems Training for Emotional Predictability and Problem Solving. This treatment was pioneered by Nancee Blum, who discovered that this program could be useful when done alongside traditional medical and psychological treatments. Two trials have shown that this method can be an excellent additional treatment for BPD. STEPPS requires a small time commitment, but based on the results, it can be well worth the effort.

STEPPS is a program that lasts for twenty-weeks and uses a two-hour session, once per week, to help groups of people with BPD learn the skills they need to address their symptoms. Two professionals lead groups that have anywhere from six to ten members. After the initial twenty-week program, participants can join another program that will meet biweekly for a year to maintain the progress they've made, while continuing to learn how to apply the skills that they have developed in the initial program.

Patients begin with an introductory description of what BPD is and how it impacts people who suffer from it. By doing this, leaders can break the stigma and begin to usher patients into the next step of teaching them the skills to deal with BPD. Family members and friends are often included in this process, and they are called the "reinforcers." They help their loved ones apply the skills that they are learning, so it is a process that includes more than just patients. People in the program track their feelings and answer questionnaires to show their progress and help them advance through the program. This program uses schemas to teach BPD patients new ways to deal with their range of emotions.

General Psychiatric Management

Many of the traditional methods of treating BPD require a lot of training and knowledge on the part of mental health professional. It can take a long time to treat and can be draining of resources. Therefore, requiring such training can make it hard to get extensive treatment for a myriad of people. Some people don't require as intense of a treatment, and General Psychiatric Management (GPM) can be a good alternative for people who don't want as an intense and focused treatment course.

GPM is a model that uses case management skills assisted by common sense that mental health professionals can easily understand and apply to patients. This method of treatment prioritizes how patients operate outside a clinical setting. It begins by explaining BPD and its symptoms to the patients and their families. Once the patient understands their condition, they can move onto beginning weekly sessions. It also monitors the kind of care that patients need going forward. If a patient has multiple treatments, GPM will coordinate those treatments. Instead of helping patients work on the roots of their issues, GPM tries to show how patients interact outside of a therapy setting.

For BPD, General Psychiatric Management uses a model of hypersensitivity, which means that patients with BPD have areas that make them sensitive, causing them to have intense emotions. Those emotions can lead to harmful behaviors like self-mutilation or suicidal actions. GPM shows patients how to be more aware of the things that cause them to be increasingly sensitive. It then works on showing them how they respond to those situations and teaches them ways to respond better in the future. Research has shown that GPM, like DBT, can result in improvements for patients with BPD when done consistently.

Natural Treatments

There are also some natural treatments that you can turn to if you want to improve your BPD. These methods won't necessarily replace seeing a mental health professional, but they can be used to lessen your symptoms and improve your lifestyle. These methods are great ways to start making changes if you are feeling apprehensive or don't have immediate access to mental health services. They are also suitable for people with mild BPD symptoms or who may not fully reach the diagnostic criteria for BPD, but still are on the BPD spectrum. If you have severe symptoms or are at risk of hurting yourself, please seek more intense care.

Several studies have suggested that your nutrition can impact your mental health. Thus, ensuring that you have proper nutrition is essential. Certain nutrients can increase your odds of reducing your symptoms. Many people with BPD benefit from increasing their levels of vitamins like vitamin C, and healthy fats like avocados or olive oil, as well as omega-3s. These foods are known for balancing moods, which can help people with BPD who have mood dysregulation. In studies, people who took omega-3 vitamins or ate fatty fish containing omega-3s had less severe symptoms, and people with low omega-3 levels had worse symptoms.

Another natural method that people have used to treat BPD is light therapy, which involves exposing oneself to a bright light that comes from a lightbox. Some people swear by this method, but there has been limited medical research on the effectiveness of this technique. You can't harm yourself by using this method, for the most part, but if you are prone to migraines, the light could trigger a headache. This treatment methodology has been found to reduce aggressive behavior and depressive feelings specifically in women with BPD.

To deal with symptoms, many people also like to bathe with Epsom salts. Epsom salts are rich in magnesium, which has been linked to relaxation and improved sleep. While an Epsom salt bath cannot cure you, it can help you to relax and calm down when your symptoms become overwhelming.

Chapter 5: How to Manage BPD

Habits Help

The habits you have make a difference in how you feel and how you behave. Good habits can result in better recovery prognoses. Habits are the subconscious parts of yourself, and you often do certain things without even thinking about it. Thus, habits can highly influence your behavior. When you have good habits, you will do healthier things more automatically. This means your life will be easier in general, so you can focus on treatment and have less to disrupt your emotionally. Habits will make you happy, healthier, and they can also reduce some of your BPD symptoms, even though they won't make them go away permanently without treatment.

Exercise can improve moods and be a great outlet for emotions. People who exercise tend to be mentally healthier. When you exercise, your body releases endorphins, which are feel-good chemicals that reduce your stress and anxiety levels. Exercise allows people with BPD to feel calmer, which can in turn help them control the anger that is inside them. Additionally, when you exercise, you can release negative energies from your body through constructive means. It can be a great choice of activity when you feel like doing something dangerous such as self-harm. Exercise allows you to challenge your body without doing things that will damage you in the long-term. Find forms of exercise that make you happy and help you feel better in your skin.

Sleep is one of the most important things that people neglect. People often claim that they are too busy to sleep, or insomnia makes it hard for them to stay and get to sleep. Nevertheless, making efforts to get adequate rest is vital for both your physical and mental health. Sleep allows your body to recover, and when you don't get it, you are more irritable. For people with emotional dysregulation, being a little grumpy can result in BPD symptoms being worsened. Being already prone to feelings things more sensitively, sleep isn't something that you can afford to miss out on. Set a time to go to bed and try to wake up at the same time each day. Developing a regular sleep schedule can have a profound impact on mental health and wellbeing.

Just like your body needs sleep, it also needs fuel to ensure that it is in top shape. Ensure that you have a balanced diet with all the macronutrients - carbs, proteins, and fats. If you struggle with making the right food choices, seek support for those specific issues. Mental health professionals and/or a nutritionist can help you with your relationship with food. If you want to improve your BPD, avoid trying fad diets and other dietary programs that will make you feel like you are missing out on foods that you love. When you feel deprived, you will be more prone to impulse. Thus, make an effort to establish a more balanced relationship with food.

Staying away from substances is a smart choice for people with BPD. People with BPD are prone to addiction and substance abuse, so keeping away from substances will benefit them greatly. Additionally, substances can exasperate the BPD symptoms that you already have, which will make them harder to control going forward. While you may feel like you have your relationship with substances under control, it's too easy to lose control without noticing that you are spiraling.

Replace bad habits with good ones. It can be hard to get rid of bad habits, but it is easier when you replace bad habits with good ones. For example, if you tend to shop impulsively, delete the app on your phone for your favorite store and replace it with an anti-anxiety game or another app that you can click into when you have the urge to do something impulsive. When the shopping app is no longer convenient, it is harder to give in to your cravings, and clicking into another app can become an excellent coping strategy. When you continue to click into the app that you've added, it will be less instinctual for you to shop. You will still have impulsive urges, but you will have a barrier that helps you resist them.

Ensure that you are maintaining good habits because those habits will make it easier to keep the lifestyle you want to live instead of the one that BPD forces on you. Good habits can help you resist your BPD urges or negative thought patterns that make it hard to be productive. Choose habits that make you feel good, not just in the short-term but also in the long term. It can take a bit of time and effort to create habits, but within a few months you can develop a handful of positive habits that will continue to serve you for years to come.

Engage with Loved Ones

Having relationships with loved ones is an essential part of life, but for people with BPD, relationships can be challenging. Let yourself trust other people as much as you can. Start with small vulnerabilities. Openness will make you feel much better about yourself, so take steps to let the people in your life in. Some people find it particularly helpful to have a loved one accompany them during certain types of therapy, as this helps the BPD individual to develop a support group of people who understand what they are going through.

Reminders

We all need reminders sometimes to ensure that we are thinking logically. Remind yourself that not everything piece of criticism is an attack on your character. People will say things that hurt you, but this doesn't always mean that something is wrong with you. Someone needing space doesn't mean that they are abandoning you. Reminders aren't going to cure BPD, but repeating them can help you alleviate some of your concerns.

Ways to Calm Down

There are several methods you can use to calm yourself down. These methods are simple tasks that anyone can do when they are feeling overwhelmed. You can use these methods as coping strategies when you are struggling to keep your emotions in check. While not all these methods will work for you, hopefully, some of them can become a part of your daily habits. Attending therapy can help you discover even more strategies that you can use to calm down, but for now, you can use some of these ones.

Take a walk. Taking a walk is great for your health, but it is also good for when you are feeling anxious or moody. If you feel a surge of emotion rushing through you, you can go on a short walk to calm down and recollect your thoughts. Walking allows you to be contemplative. It lets you to slow down your mind and process information that you might otherwise struggle to process.

Write in a journal. Journaling is a great process that can help you work through your feelings in a creative and fun way. When you journal, you are more likely to act upon your aspirations. Further, it gives you a place to be vulnerable with yourself. You can admit to things that you've held secretly in your head. Putting those ideas on paper feels confessional and can be a great stepping-stone to sharing information with your loved ones. People who journal have more mental clarity, and they can find patterns in their behaviors and determine the things that most set them off. Journaling just fifteen minutes a day can change your life and your mental health.

Do something productive. When you're feeling destructive urges, find something constructive to do instead. Open your journal and write a short story. Go for a run or lift some weights. Make dinner for someone you love. Get out in the yard and do some gardening. Do activities that will help you in the long-term rather than just give you temporary satisfaction.

When you're feeling off, call a friend. You don't need to tell them what is going on with you if you don' feel comfortable, but if you can call someone who means a lot to you, that can be a great distraction from your feelings. Social experiences can take away some of the negative emotions that you have, and it can help to feel that you are not alone. You can talk about anything you want — serious or not serious — as long as you are talking in a way that relieves your worries rather than building them up. Know the friends you can call when you are going through a hard time, and if you feel comfortable, tell them that sometimes you may need to call to stop your mental health from spiraling. Good friends will understand and be happy to help you.

Set a timer and sit with your emotions. For ten minutes, tell yourself that you will delay acting on the thoughts that urge you to engage in destructive behaviors. When you force yourself to sit with your problems, you can start to deal with them rather than trying to escape them. When you take the time to sit and let your thoughts run their course, they will lose their power over you, and you will eventually calm down. Eventually, these feelings will calm. If after 10 minutes you aren't feeling better, either try for another 10-minutes, or engage in some exercise or other productive activity that will be able to clear your mind.

Hold an ice cube or another cold object in your hand if you start to feel yourself dissociate or if you want to self-harm. In both cases, an ice cube can transform your mental process. An ice cube can help ground you and keep you mentally present. Let yourself feel the coldness, and remind yourself that you are still present and still in your body. As an alternative method, you can snap a rubber band against your wrist (just enough to feel it but not enough to hurt yourself). These methods can help you from resorting to more harmful methods or mindsets that you will regret later.

Take some deep breaths. Take a few moments when you feel overwhelmed to let your breathing steady. When you aren't breathing deeply, it can be hard to feel secure and calm. Accordingly, allowing yourself to step aside and breathe puts you back in a more relaxed state. Your breath is directly linked to your autonomic nervous system, and by consciously controlling it, you will be able to relax and calm both your body and mind.

Listen to music. Music is one of the best methods for dealing with your moods. Create different playlists for different moods and let yourself get lost in the playlist. Find songs that you can relate to or that make you feel a boost of positivity. Most people respond well to music, and it can have a transformative effect on your mental health.

Use a stress ball. People with BPD are prone to feeling rage, whether it is internalized or externalized. Thus, having a stress ball near you can be good to squeeze out your worries or fears. You can use the stress ball to take out your feelings instead of taking it out on yourself or others.

Staying calm can be hard when you have BPD and you feel your emotions surge. There are so many methods that you can use to feel less anxious. The main thing you need to remember is to avoid coping mechanisms that will cause you long-term or short-term harm, because those mechanisms will only worsen your BPD. Incorporating just a few of these coping mechanisms can make your self-destructive tendencies less harmful and reduce the power of BPD over you.

Conclusion

Borderline personality disorder is one of the most misunderstood mental health issues, which is unfortunate and unfair to sufferers. Thus, it can be incredibly hard to navigate for those who struggle with it. Throughout this book you've learned the basics of BPD, and now should have a good understanding of what this condition involves.

Remember, if you feel as though you might have borderline personality disorder – never self-diagnose.
I urge you to seek out the advice of a medical professional to receive an accurate diagnosis, and to begin creating a treatment plan.

With more studies about borderline personality disorder taking place, we are slowly learning more about this difficult condition, and how to best treat it.
As you have now learned, there are some promising treatment modalities currently available that can provide great relief for those with BPD.

My hope is that you now feel well educated on this condition and have a good understanding of the different signs and symptoms associated with it, as well as the various treatments and coping strategies that can be used to combat it. Thank you for taking the time to learn more about borderline personality disorder. I wish you the best of luck!

CPSIA information can be obtained
at www.ICGtesting.com
Printed in the USA
LVHW081756270821
696279LV00011B/183